WELCOME

THIS ANNUAL BELONGS TO:

....

MINI MYSTERY

There are **10** hidden mud monster footprints in this Annual that could be vital clues. Help find them and list the page numbers below.

Contents

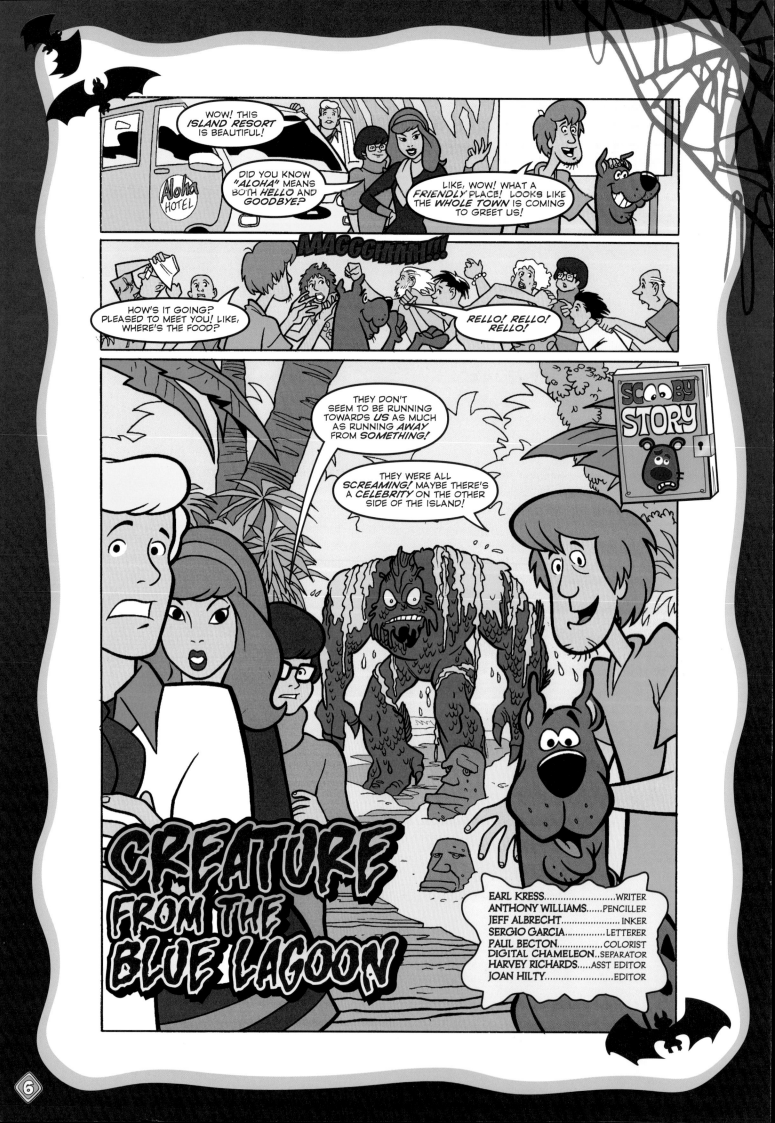

CREATURE FROM THE BLUE LAGOON

EARL KRESS.....................WRITER
ANTHONY WILLIAMS......PENCILLER
JEFF ALBRECHT...................INKER
SERGIO GARCIA.............LETTERER
PAUL BECTON................COLORIST
DIGITAL CHAMELEON..SEPARATOR
HARVEY RICHARDS.....ASST EDITOR
JOAN HILTY.......................EDITOR

CONTINUED ON PAGE 14

11

Zombie Pirate Ship!

Is there anything scarier than zombies or pirates? Well how about ZOMBIE PIRATES! Get ready to tour the most putrid pirate ship ever to sail the seven seas, courtesy of Mystery Inc. Terror Tours!

Zombie Pirates

This band of brain-eating buccaneers just LOVE fighting and plundering! And when there's no-ne else around, they fight each other and plunder their OWN ship!

MYSTERY INC. TERROR TOURS

Sea Monster

Ship's Anchor

Mouldy Wine Storage

Things to spot:
- 3 Treasure chests ☐
- 5 members of Mystery Inc. ☐
- A treasure map ☐

Putrid Parrots

Zombie Captain

Treasure Chamber
All the stolen treasure is locked away in this room, and only the Captain has the key. Otherwise his own crew would steal it all!

Skull Cannon

The Plank

13

MUMMY MONEYBOX!

Keep your pocket money safe inside this spooky mummy's tomb!

You will need:
a water bottle, kitchen paper, cardboard, old newspapers, PVA glue, sticky tape, white bandages, scissors, pencil, paints and paintbrush.

1

Roll up a ball of kitchen paper and place it on the top of the water bottle to make the mummy's head. Roll up four sausages of kitchen paper to make arms and legs and fix them onto the bottle with sticky tape.

2

Cover the mummy with two layers of torn-up kitchen paper and diluted PVA glue. Then cut strips of white bandage and wrap it around the mummy. The wet glue will hold it in place.

3

Cut an oval shape from card. Repeat so that you have two. Cut a square hole in the middle of one of them.

4

Cut a strip of card about 7cm wide and long enough to go around the oval without the hole. Stick it in place with sticky tape. This will make the basic shape of the mummy's tomb.

5

Take the other oval with the hole cut out of it and push it half way inside the mummy's tomb. Tape it in place. This will make a secret compartment for your money to be stored. When you want to empty the box, you can shake the money out of the square hole!

6

Cover the box with a layer of torn-up newspaper and glue and leave it to dry. Cut a slot at the top for your money. Now you can paint the tomb and decorate it with spooky hieroglyphics! Place the mummy inside the tomb and your money box is ready to go!

ON THE RUN!

The gang need your help to get this mystery solved! Work out which member of Mystery. Inc. is on the right path to capturing the crook.

ANSWER: Velma catches the crook!

ALL MY TOMORROWS

FRANK STROM-WRITER • **ROBERT POPE**-PENCILLER
DAVE HUNT-INKER • NICK J. NAPOLITANO-LETTERER • HEROIC AGE-COLORIST
HARVEY RICHARDS-ASST EDITOR• JOAN HILTY-EDITOR

WE'D HEARD ABOUT THE *MYSTERIOUS ACCIDENTS* YOU'VE BEEN HAVING AND WE DECIDED TO *INVESTIGATE*--!

AMATEUR DETECTIVES?!? NO WAY! I'VE GOT A *TIGHT SCHEDULE* AND I CAN'T HAVE *NOSY KIDS* DISRUPTING IT! GET OUT!

GOSH, VELMA AND THE GANG ARE FRIENDS OF MINE. CAN'T THEY *STAY*? THEY COULD WORK AS *ASSISTANTS*... OR GOFERS!

WHATEVER! JUST SO LONG AS THEY DON'T GET IN THE WAY!

GULP! DO WE *REALLY* HAVE TO... WORK?

OF COURSE! THIS WAY YOU CAN *SNOOP* BEHIND THE SCENES. SWEEP UP THE *MESS* AND SEE IF YOU CAN LEARN ANYTHING ABOUT THIS SO-CALLED *SHADOW MONSTER*.

SURE...A LITTLE *WORK* NEVER HURT ANYBODY.

RRRI'M HURT RRALREADY! WHIMPER!

WOW! I CAN'T BELIEVE I'M ACTUALLY ON THE SET OF *"ALL MY TOMORROWS"*! IT'S MY *FAVORITE* SOAP OPERA! I NEVER MISS IT!

A BIG FAN, HUH? THEN MAYBE YOU KNOW SOMETHING ABOUT THIS GHOST OR MONSTER OR WHATEVER IT IS?

WHO'S *THAT*?

ERICA SLAYZAK-- SHE'S BEEN ON THIS SHOW FOR *TWENTY-FOUR YEARS*!

27

CONTINUED ON PAGE 32

CREEPY QUIZ!

Give this devilishly difficult quiz a whirl and discover how your spooky spirit scores!

1 On what night of the year does Hallowe'en fall?

2 By what other name is a yeti known by?

3 True or false - the vampire bat is vegetarian.

4 Which of these is a Hallowe'en game?
a) banana bobbing
b) apple bobbing

5 Can you work out what these spooky clues are talking about?
a) a see-through spook that rhymes with toast
b) a cackling ghoul that rhymes with rich
c) a monster with stitches that rhymes with mine

6 What's the name of the Scottish lake which is home to a monster?

True or false, spiders have eight eyes.

8 What is a banshee?
a) a goblin
b) a ghost

9 What is a Jack O'Lantern?

10 Which Hallowe'en ghoul would own a black cat?

11 What kind of ghoul is Count Dracula?
a) werewolf
b) vampire

12 What kind of building does a mummy live in?

13 Is a pumpkin a fruit, an animal or a vegetable?

29

A CREEPY CASTLE!

The Castle...

Begin by drawing the simple building blocks for your castle, as shown in steps 1-3.

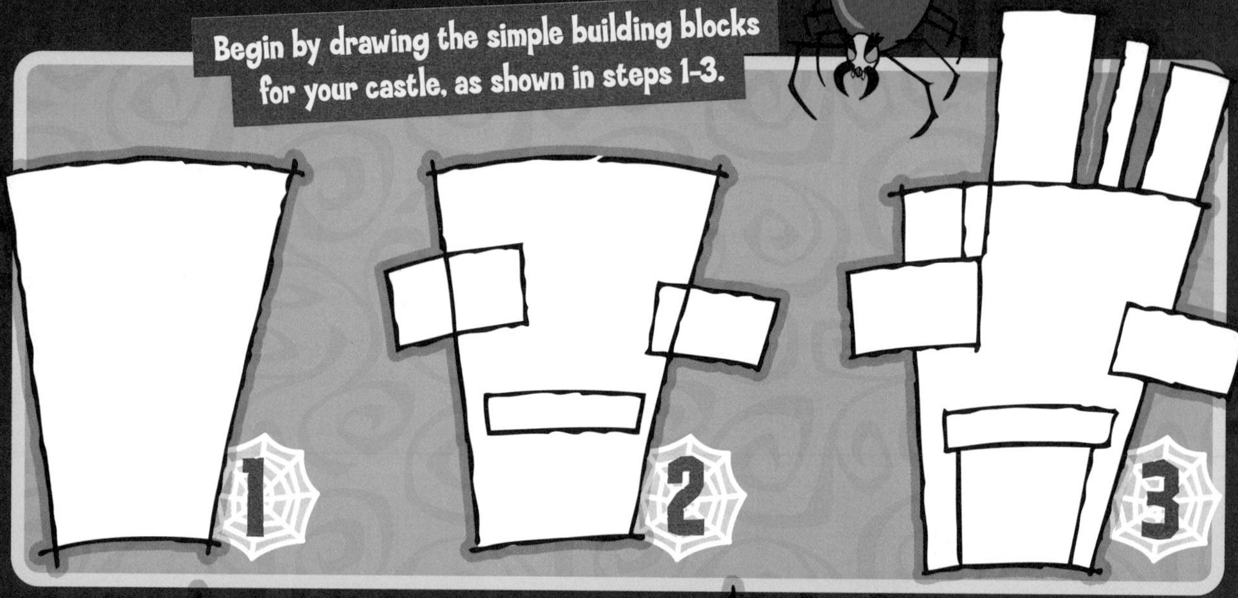

1

2

3

TIP: Draw in light pencil to start with, as you'll need to rub some lines out as you go!

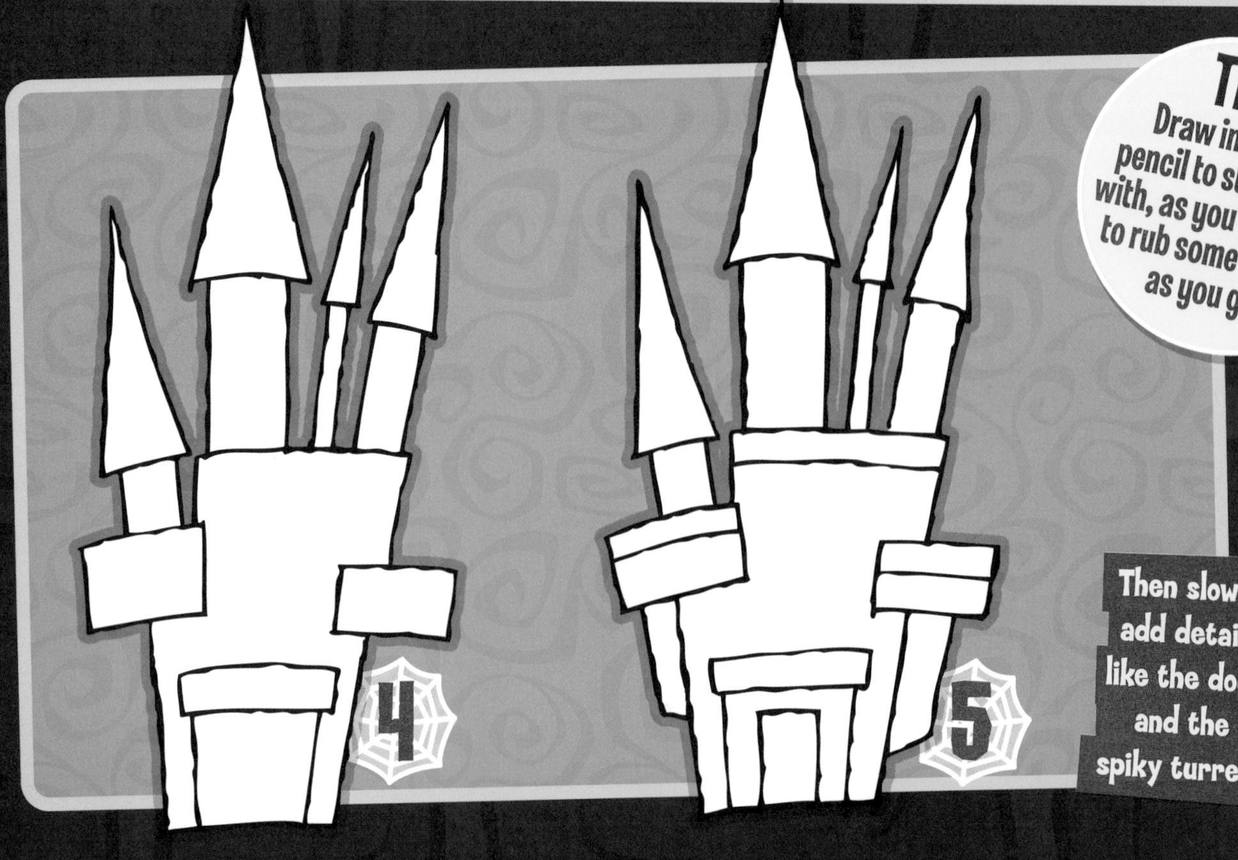

4

5

Then slowly add detail, like the door and the spiky turrets.

Now draw in the windows, ledges and a hill to stand on.

6

TIP:
If you go wrong, just start again. Practice makes perfect!

7

Now rub out the turrets and redraw them so they're weird and wonky!
Finally add a few more bricks, a moon and some murky mountains!

Terrifying Tree!

How about a terrifying tree to go next to your castle? Just follow these four steps!

1 **2** **3** **4**

CONTINUED FROM PAGE 28

Clued Up!

Mystery Machine Mix-Up!

Help Fred to work out which van is the real Mystery Machine.

A B C D

Say It Again!

Everyone's talking at the same time and poor Scooby can't work out who is saying what! Can you lend him an ear and work it out?

1 Like, go grab me a banana split sandwich, Scoob!

2 I'd have gotten away with it if it weren't for that pesky dog!

3 Would you do it for a Scooby Snack?

4 Scooby will be the bait in my monster trap!

5 Jeepers, Scooby, there's a ghost right behind you!

A B C D E

CREEPY COLOUR!

Grab your colouring pens and go colour crazy on this scary scene!

BATS° WHAT I'M AFRAID OF

BRETT LEWIS- WRITER   PAUL BECTON-COLORIST
JOE STATON- PENCILS   DIGITAL CHAMELEON-SEPARATIONS
DAVE HUNT- INKS   HARVEY RICHARDS- ASST. EDITOR
RYAN CLINE- LETTERER   JOAN HILTY- EDITOR

CONTINUED ON PAGE 50

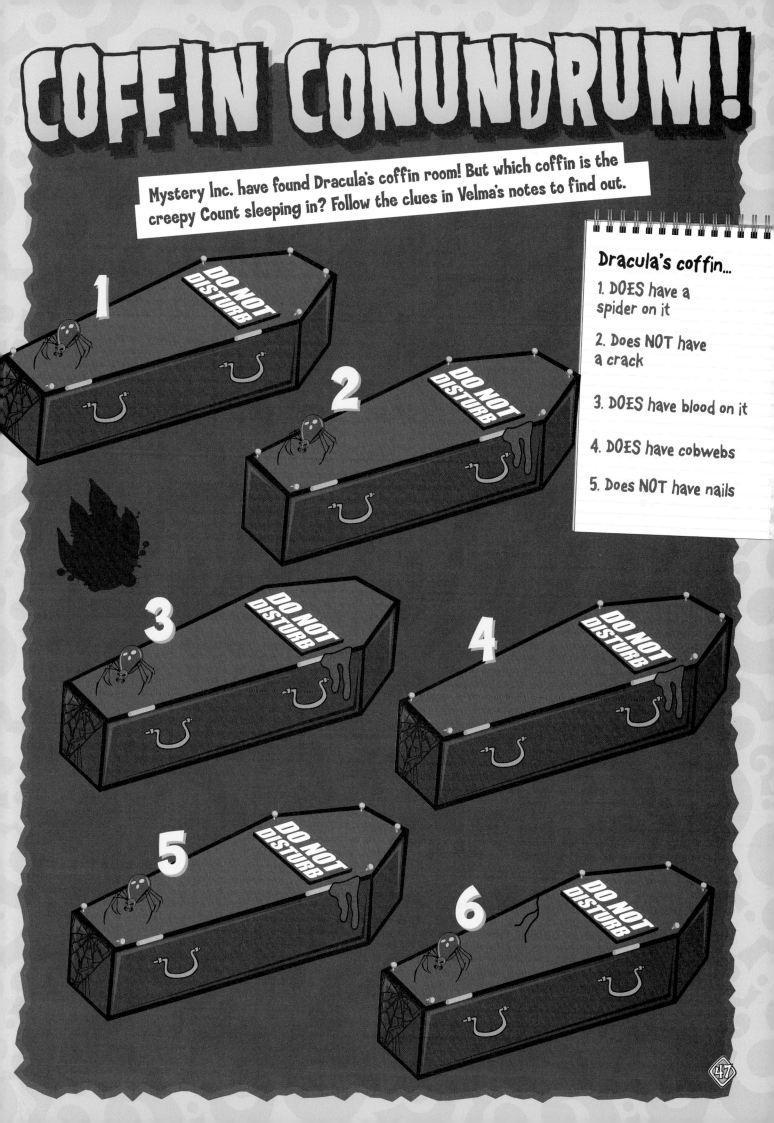

MEMORY MASH!

Study this swampy scene for one minute, trying to remember everything you see. Then cover it up and answer the questions to the right!

QUESTION TIME!

Tick the correct answers!

1. Which monster were Scooby, Fred and Shaggy running away from?

A.   B.   C.

2. Who else from Mystery Inc. was hiding?

A. Daphne   B. Velma   C. No-one

3. How many zombie hands were rising from the ground?

A. Four   B. Three   C. Two

4. What had Shaggy dropped?

A.   B.   C.

5. What colour were the toadstools?

A.   B.   C.

6. How many spiders were there?

A.   B.   C.

49

SPOOK SPOTTER!

The gang are investigating a creepy ancient castle! Can you help them spot all the spooks?

56

Tick as you find...

- [ ] 11 bats
- [ ] 8 evil knights
- [ ] 6 rats
- [ ] 5 skeleton hands
- [ ] 4 freaky paintings
- [ ] 2 giant spiders

Bonus Items!

- [ ] A ghostly face in a mirror
- [ ] Scooby hiding
- [ ] A message from Shaggy 'Zoinks!'

57

THE MYSTERY OF CREEPY CASTLE!

Are you brave enough to say 'boo' to a ghost?
Then Mystery, Inc. need your help solving this ghoulish mystery!

The place: Creepy Castle, Spookton Road, Battyton, Ghoulshire.

The mystery: A vampire is rumoured to live in Creepy Castle and the local people are terrified to go near it. A precious golden goblet has been stolen from the local museum. Is there a link? Mystery, Inc. have been called in to investigate....

TRUE OR FALSE?

Your first challenge is to brush up on your vampire knowledge. Are these statements true or false?

1. Vampires are afraid of garlic
....

2. Vampires are vegetarians
....

3. Count Docular is a famous vampire
....

4. Bats are a vampire's favourite pet
....

CRYPTIC CLUE

The gang split up, and you investigate The Haunted Library. You discover a book written in code ... it's a clue! Unscramble the words to reveal the hidden message.

CODE BREAKER

A	B	C	D
E	F	G	H
I	J	K	L
M	N	O	P
Q	R	S	T
U	V	W	X
Y	Z		

58

IN THE FRAME

The vampire has hidden the goblet behind one of these portraits. Each portrait has an identical pair except for one, and that is where the booty is hidden! Help Fred to find it.

A C E H

B D F G I

CATCH THAT CROOK!

BORIS
THE CASTLE GARDENER

ETHEL
THE MUSEUM CARETAKER

HUMPHREY
THE MUSEUM CURATOR

Now that you have found the treasure and tracked down that blood-sucking baddie, it's time to unmask his true identity. Make your way through the maze to discover which of the three suspects is behind this crazy crime!

Congratulations! You've solved the mystery of Creepy Castle. Thanks for all your help!

Answers: True or false - 1. true 2. false 3. false, it's Count Dracula 4. true. Cryptic clue - The vampire is hiding in the dungeon. In the frame - frame E. Catch that crook - Humphrey the museum curator is the crook.

MYSTERY MONSTER!

Find out which monster is hiding in these lines by shading each shape with a dot inside!

ANSWER: MUMMY

THERE'S SOMETHING OUT THERE!

Strange shadows keep moving outside the window! Can you spot who's who by matching each character to their shadow?